Tree-
House
Comix
Proudly
Presents

CAT KID
COMIC CLUB
Perspectives

WRITTEN, ILLUSTRATED, AND COLORED BY

DAV PILKEY

AS GEORGE BEARD AND HAROLD HUTCHINS

WITH DIGITAL COLOR BY JOSE GARIBALDI

graphix

AN IMPRINT OF

■SCHOLASTIC

Library of Congress Control Number 2021932630

978-1-338-78485-5 (POB)   978-1-338-78486-2 (Library)

10 9 8 7 6 5 4 3 2 1   21 22 23 24 25

Printed in China   62
First edition, December 2021

Illustrations and hand lettering by Dav Pilkey

Clay and paper models, Japanese calligraphy, photography,
poetry, and paper cutouts by Dav Pilkey

All mini comics (except BABY FLIPPY) colored by Dav Pilkey using acrylic paints,
colored pencils, ballpoint pens, markers, crayons, gouache, and watercolors.

Digital Color by Jose Garibaldi | Flatting by Aaron Polk
Special Thanks to: Arcana Izu and Asaba Ryokan

Editor: Ken Geist | Editorial Team: Megan Peace and Jonah Newman
Book design by Dav Pilkey and Phil Falco
Creative Director: Phil Falco
Publisher: David Saylor

CHAPTERS & COMICS

To my Mother, Barbara Pilkey,
and my Okaa-san, Yayoi Chiba

With two perspectives...
Warming sun and cooling rain
many flowers bloom

- D.P.

CHAPTER 1

What's up, Guys?

Welcome back to the **Second** week of...

...The CAT KiD COMiC CLUB!

HOORAY!!!

I know you all worked hard last weekend!

Does anybody have something they'd like to share?

OH! OH! OH! OH! OH!

Okay, Melvin.

Naomi's kicking me!

I AM NOT!

And now she's LYING!

NAOMI, KEEP YOUR FEET TO YOURSELF!

It looks pretty cool to me!

...but if you guys think it's **Boring**...

No! No! We want to learn how to write our names like that! Yeah!

Say you're sorry, Drake! Sorry!

Alright, then!

Hey, I need your eraser.

Rub Rub Rub

Rub Rub Rub

Don't use it ALL UP!!!

Rub Rub Rub

23

And, NAOMI?

You can Go sit on the Time-Out Rock!

WHY? WHaT DiD I DO?

Oh, wait. I Remember now.

OK, See Ya!!!

Time OUT.

ALRIGHT, YOU GUYS...

WE'RE GONNA START OVER TOMORROW...

...SO YA better QUIT GOOFING AROUND!!!

Don't worry, Molly. We won't Goof around tomorrow...

And that's a PROMISE!!!

CHAPTER 2

MORE GOOFING AROUND

The next day...

HEY!

You kids PROMISED to behave YOURSELVES TODAY!!!

We know.

But we didn't really mean it.

Yeah. We just say stuff sometimes.

Okay, if You want to Goof around...

... and **BREAK PROMISES**...

...then Li'l Petey can Go home...

... and You can all spend the rest of the day...

DOING CHORES!

Uh, no thanks.

We'll be Good.

Yeah. We'd rather make comics than do chores!

Wow.

Their enthusiasm warms my heart.

OKAY, GUYS, TODAY IS A DO-OVER!

But before we begin...

...Does Anybody have A COMIC they'd like to share?

WE DO! WE DO!

TIME WASTERS: wasters of time

We made a Comic last NiGht!!!

41

CHUBBS McSPIDERBUTT

WRITTEN AND DIRECTED BY The HACKER BROS.

Once there was a Guy named Chubbs...

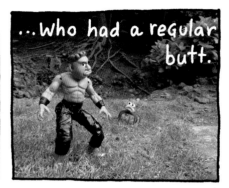

...who had a regular butt.

Then one day he accidentally sat on a **SPIDER** named Jake.

PLOP!

OUCHIES!

You bit MY BUTT!

Sowwy!

Well **NOW** what am I supposed to do?

You could be a superhero!!!

Hey! That's a Good idea!!!

Thanks, Jake!

No Prob!

So Jake and Chubbs bought an old van...

...and customized it!

CHUBBS & Jake

This van has it **ALL !!!!!**

CHUBBS & JAKE

Smiley-faced Grill?

Check!

Froyo-Smoothie Station?

Check!

CHUBBS & JAKE

CHUBBS & JAKE

Indoor Disco Dance Studio?

Check!

Well, we did it, Jake!

We can be heroes!

CHUBBS & JAKE

Can I be your sidekick, Chubbs?

You bet, little buddy!

But WAIT! ... What's this?

WHOOOOSH!

CHUBBS & JAKE

If you want to be in this club...

...then you need to **FOCUS!**

I'll try.

Your breath is stinky.

THAT'S PERFECT! —but say it to **THEM,** Not **ME!**

His breath is stinky! **SCOTT!**

WiLL the N.V.N.C. Prevail?

WiLL our heroes Get their feelings hurt?

WiLL Scott ever Learn to be Rude?

Find out **Soon** in our **NEXT** chapter:

ChUBBS McSPiDERBUTT 2
The Birth of BiG BubbA BabyheAD

'Cuz You always try to be the **BOSS** of Everybody!

Besides, we're the **HACKER BROTHERS!**

GENDER DISCRIMINATION!

WHAT'S GOING ON NOW?

They won't let me work with them 'cuz I'm a **GIRL!**

WHO WON'T?

Gilbert and Rico and Drake!!!

...We discriminate against **EVERYbody!**

You shouldn't Say it like that!

Oh.

Naomi, I can't **Force** them to work with You.

OKAY, FiNE!

I'LL MAKE MY OWN COMIC!

...AND it'LL be **WAY** Better thaп YOURS!

CHAPTER 3

New Day, New Perspective

OKAY, GUYS! Today is a new day...

...and **This Time,** We're Gonna be **SERIOUS!!!**

So **NO FIGHTING...** **NO TATTLING...**

...And **NO TIME WASTING!**

aw, maaan!

So—does anybody have a new comic to share?

WE DO!

HOORAY!!!

That was AWESOME!

Aw, maaaan!!!

We tried our best to fail...

...but I guess we didn't succeed!!!

You just blew my mind, dude.

Well, I think it's **GREAT** that you kids are **IMPROVING!**

Even your **DRAWINGS** Are Getting better!

Look at the **PERSPECTIVE** on this building!

Curly drew that, not me.

Hey, Curly, can you show us how to draw like that?

Okay!

First, you draw the Ground...

...then, You make a building, which is just a rectangle.

Then, add some Square windows.

Now, put a dot on the Ground...

...and draw a line from the edge...

...to the dot.

If you want, you can add windows on the side.

Just draw the sides of each window...

...and connect the tops and bottoms of each side...

...to the dot.

Now, draw the other side of each window...

...then erase all of the extra lines.

Rub
Rub
Rub

CHAPTER 4

Big Trouble for Little Melvin

I'm the only kid in our family with a **PERFECT RECORD!**

And I'd like to keep it that way!!!

Can I do a **Different Punishment?**

I could write sentences... or do extra chores...

No, Melvin. I think you need—

AW, DADDY, PLEEEASE?

It WASN'T even MY FAULT!!!

SHE Started it!

All I wanted to do was Draw with **Perspective!!!**

Melvin, **PERSPECTIVE** isn't just About **DRAWING!!!**

It's also about **UNDERSTANDING!**

It's about seeing the world from Someone **ELSE'S** Point of view!!!

Hey!

Would You still like to do a **Different Punishment?**

Time out.

Yes! Yes! Yes! Yes! Ye

Okay. Then You can make a comic...

...About Naomi...

...from **HER PERSPECTIVE!**

AND it Better NOT BE MEAN!

CHAPTER 5

How am I **EVER** Gonna finish this?

I Know! Write about how much You love me!

I Don't Love You!

You don't?

NO! You're the most Annoying frog in the **Whole World!**

So if some big monster came out of those woods...

CHAPTER 6

Sister Stories

And so...

HEY! You kids are **LATE!**

It was h<u>i</u>s fault!

WAS NOT!!!

Well, you missed the first part of Poppy's new comic!

It's okay, Molly!

I'll start over!

One time there was a really, really old Dog...

...Who died.

KLUNK

And everybody was sad and stuff.

OLD DOG

But they didn't need to be...

OLD DOG

...because they didn't know...

While they Flew...

...Skelopup got sleepier...

... and sleepier.

Soon he was dreaming of his old Life.

He dreamed about Fun stuff...

... and happy stuff ...

... and sad stuff.

HOW TO DRAW Skelopup
in 14 supa easy steps.

How to DRAW

The Little Ghost Girl

in 14 Supa easy steps

ABOUT THE CREATOR:

POPPY

POPPY is a FroG who Likes to make up Ghost stories. She also Likes Pizza but with **NO** cheese because she is Lactose intolerant and it makes ~~me~~ her throw up.

Wow, Poppy! That was **AWESOME!**

Thanks!

Any other thoughts?

I liked the "TACO Death" Restaurant!

Me too!

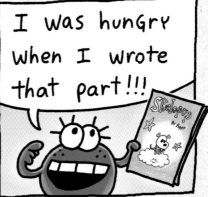

I was hungry when I wrote that part!!!

Is that what **REALLY** happens when you die?

Beats me! I was just using my imagination.

Oh.

Okay, who's next?

I made a comic with Wendy!!!

It's all about Daddy's Amazing Adventures...

...When he was just a little baby!

I drew the pictures...

...and I adapted the story!

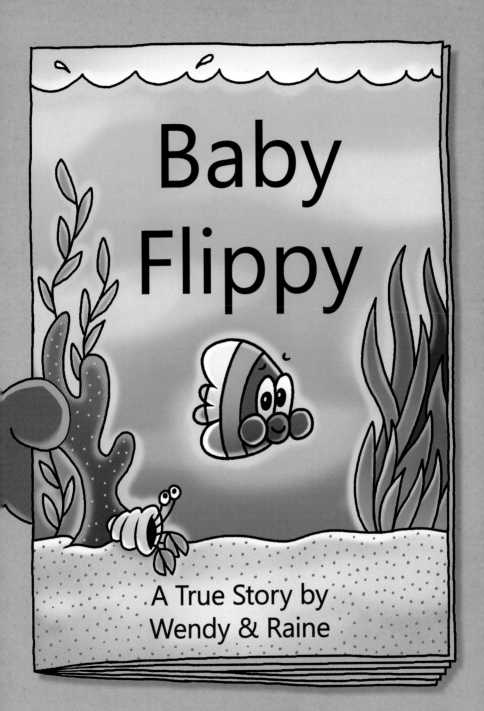

Baby
Flippy

A True Story by
Wendy & Raine

ALRIGHT, ALRIGHT!

SETTLE down, YA WEIRDOS!

Wendy and Raine just ended their comic **DRAMATICALLY!**

That's called a **CLIFFHANGER!**

It makes readers **excited** to **RETURN** to the next episode!

It Just made Me **MAD!!!**

Yeah! Me too!!!

Can we say **"BASED"** on a true story?

I Guess that Would be okay.

Sweeeet!!!

Things Are Gonna Get **SPICY!!!**

Does Anybody else have a Comic to Share?

We made a new **HAIKU-PHOTO COMIC!**

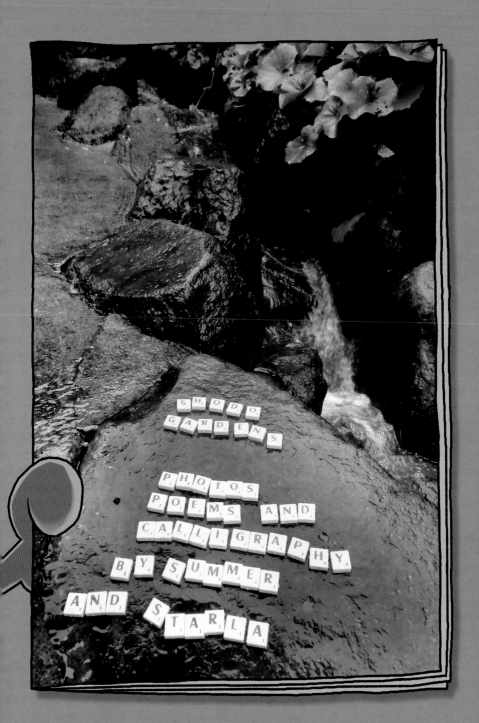

SHODO GARDENS

PHOTOS POEMS AND CALLIGRAPHY BY SUMMER AND STARLA

little blade of grass
even though the world is hard
you have found a way

努力

one good photograph
comes to those who dare to take
a thousand bad ones

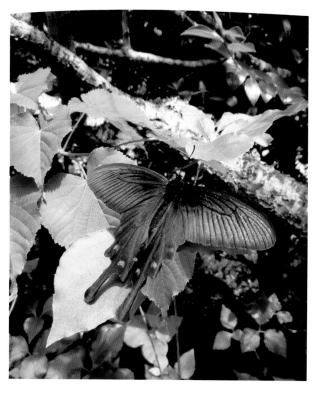

閉

bold, black butterfly
spread your wings in the morning
and bathe in the sun

自
信

if you're the pink one
don't worry about the rest.
just be the pink one

花火

garden fireworks
bursting bright in clouds of moss
nature celebrates

Haiku and Shodo
are types of Japanese art
with structure and rules.

but with these two arts,
feeling is more important
than anything else.

one must know the rules
in order to move past them.
learn, then step beyond...

Each Shodo character can have many meanings. These are some meanings for the ones we painted:

道　Way, means, road

努
力　Try hard + Power
= Endeavor

開　Open or unfold

自
信　Self-confidence
[+ Trust]

花
火　Flower + Fire
= Fireworks

Nao'omi Kuratani, Akemi Kobayashi, Shunsuke Okunishi, *A New Dictionary of Kanji Usage* (Tokyo: Gakken Co., LTD, 1982).

Summer and Starla would like to acknowledge and thank the artists who inspired them recently, including:

Shoko Kanazawa, who is one of Japan's most highly respected Shodo artists. She paints from her heart with giant brushes. She also has Down's syndrome.

And

Shozo Sato, author of *Shodo: The Quiet Art of Japanese Zen Calligraphy* (Rutland: Tuttle Publishing, 2014).

Wow! That was **COOOOOL!!!**

Thanks!

I liked those stick drawings!

They're not sticks. They're Japanese words.

Oh.

Will you show us how to write them?

No way! I'm too shy.

I'll do it!!!

We learned it from a library book!

First, you get your watercolors and a brush...

...add some water...

...then you gotta get your **MIND** ready!

Take deep breaths...

CHAPTER 7
THE INSPIRATION

It's mostly Melvin and Naomi's fault!!!

Yeah!

Thanks A **Lot**, You Guys!!!

We can't have a party because of **You Two!!!**

Yeah!

Gee whiz! I feel **Sooo Terrible...**

...I'm Gonna Go cry now.

HEY, SLUGGER!

Do you want to win some balloons for your Girlfriend?

She's my sister!

Just Give it a shot, buddy!!!

I'll Give You a balloon for each can You Knock over!

OKAY!

WHOOSH!

Give it another try, sport!!!

SWOOOF

... and dopes like you **Never even NoTice!!!**

Is that why you hate me so much?

I don't hate you.

You're, like, the world's most funnest person to fight with!

CHAPTER 8

The Saddest Friday of All Time

The next day...

Where the heck are Melvin and Naomi?

Yeah! They were supposed to be here **TEN MINUTES AGO!**

THIS is why we're **NOT** having a party!

You kids have been **VERY NAUGHTY** this week!!!

FIGHTING... WASTING Time...

Well that was depressing.

Hey! Let's all cheer Daddy up!

Good idea!

Come on, Gang!

Let's Go!!!

We're sorry, Daddy.

I know.

It's not **YOUR** fault that we're naughty!

I blame society!

Me too!

Squid Kid and Katydid

by Molly and Li'l Petey

meanwhile, at Bug School...

.. Katydid was also having trouble.

Everyone else sat still...

...but Katydid didn't.

Boing

Everyone else paid attention...

...but Katydid didn't.

SWISH

Everyone else learned the same way...

C A T C A T C A T

...but Katydid didn't.

And so...

You're a misfit!

Yeah!

Beat it, Katydid!!!

Run, Squid Kid, Run!!!

Jump, Katydid, Jump!!!

And then...

Squid kid felt unsure...

... but Katydid didn't.

Squid kid felt Afraid...

...but katydid didn't.

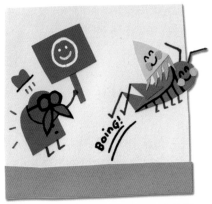
Boing!

After a hard day of changing the WORLD...

BOING   BOING   BOING

...They bounced to SQuid kid's house.

S.K.

SQuid kid's Parents made pizza.

Then Squid kid said:

Do you want to be my BFF?

and katydid...

...did.

The END

Well then Get ready to **RAISE** the **ROOF** with **JOY**, Daddy...

...because it's time for...

BABY FROG SQUAD!

OH, YEAH! OH, YEAH!

WHOOP! WHOOP! BABY FROG SQUAD iN THE HOUSE!!!

OH, YEAH! GIMME SOME! OH, YEAH!

Once upon a time...

...there were three baby frogs...

...who went to the Police Academy.

Cops "я" us

Frankie mastered Martial Arts...

CRACK

... C.C. mastered mechanical Arts...

CRANK CRANK CRANK

TOOLS

...and Boo mastered the art of witty Retorts.

I know You Are, but what am I?

HAW HAW

But soon they Got tired of working for the man.

I Know! Let's be Space heroes instead!

O.K.

...So Frankie, C.C. and Boo built a rocket ship...

...And they blasted off.

BOING

Soon, danger
was detected on Planet #39.

Oh, No!!! It's A
BiG, Bad BULLY!!!

Let's Go!

PLanet
#39

So they landed...

FSSHHHHH

KLONK

Soon our heroes met up with the bully.

Hey! CUT it OUT!

Get Lost, worm breath!

I Know You are, but what am I?

That **Never** Gets old!

Soon, Frankie, C.C., and Boo were **CORNERED!**

Bye-bye, Baby Frogs!

Why do you gotta be so evil, Brutus?

It's not my fault.

I was programmed to be evil!

Do You know who **ELSE** could use some Love???

Whisper whisper whisper

That's a **GREAT** idea!

Tee-hee!

Our work is done!

HOORAY!!!

And so...

ZOOM

Our first mission was a **SUPA SUCCESS!**

Yeah... but I sure will miss that little Pink robot.

I Wonder if we'll ever see Brutus AGAIN?

Find out in the **NEXT** issue of:

BABY FROG SQUAD

COMING SOON!

ABOUT THE CREATORS:

Billie likes to make up stories and watch videos. She also likes sports and spiders.

El likes birds and dragonflies. They sing in a punk rock band with their brothers, Pink and Curly. It's called: "The Eye Screams."

Deb likes to make friendship bracelets and origami. She designed the characters in this comic.

Frida likes cereal.

194

Well? What did ya think, Daddy?

I thought it was **WONDERFUL!**

Thank You all for cheering me up!!!

Now Let's Go home and have a snack!

YAY!

This wasn't such a Sad Friday after all!

I Know! This chapter's title was **WAY OFF!**

CHAPTER 9
NAOMI AND MELVIN
REDEEM THEMSELVES
(SORT OF)

A few minutes Later...

HEY! Where were You two?

We were working on our comics!

I finished my Punishment comic!

Do You want to see it?

Of course!!!

FEAST YOUR EYEBALLS!!!

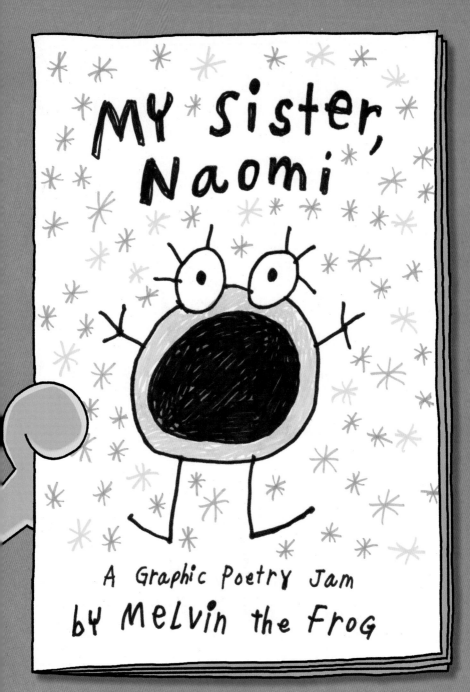

This is a jam about my **Sister**

and the **Mister**

Who **dismissed her.**

Just a fool at the **Fair**
who didn't **Care.**
Didn't see her **There.**
He didn't see the **Writer.**
The **Fighter.**
The **Fire Lighter.**

Didn't see the rage inside her
when injustices **ignite her.**

He thought he knew it **ALL**.
Thought the Girl was **small**.
Didn't **stop** to **cop** the meaning
                    of it **ALL**.

The sting of the killer **Bees**...
The thorn on the **Trees**...
The virus, the **disease**...

They're **ALL**
so **small**
that nobody **sees**
But watch out, **Y'ALL**,
Because they'll bring ya to your
knees.

His Gray
Matter
May be
Flatter...

...but **hey,**
it's **okay.**
He wasn't using
it **Anyway.**

So Go on, be a **hater.**
Underestimate her.
But you better **Pray**
you **Stay**
outta her **Way!**

'Cuz like the **FLY** said to the little **Spider,**

As she **tied** her web a little **tighter:**

"I Guess I shoulda **Tried** to be a little **Brighter.**"

Too Late. He's **dried.** and ended up **inside her.**

I'm not Gonna **Make** that **Mistake...**

That's why I'll always fight **Beside her.**

Bonk

The END!!!

A **M**elvin's **M**edia **M**egacorp Production

Written by: Melvin   Art production by: Melvin
Drawings by: Melvin   Copyedited by: Melvin
Edited by: Melvin   backgrounds by: Melvin
Costumes by: Melvin   Coloring by: Melvin
Lettering by: Melvin   Publicity by: Melvin
          Based on an original idea by: Melvin
Copyright by: Melvin. All rights reserved by: Melvin
Time-out rock sat on by: everybody EXCEPT MELVIN

Lou and Rose...

...would not wear clothes...

...but Grandma had a plan.

Underwear is Fun to wear!!!

...and then the Joy Began.

But very soon, beneath the moon...

They came upon a sight!

For Down below a Fashion show...

Monster Fashion show

...had turned into a FIGHT!!!

Monster Fashion Show

"I Am Dressed the Very Best!"
Each angry Monster said.

But Grandma knew just what to do...

... to change their minds instead.

What will she do...

(with Rose and Lou)

...to stop this crazy game?

And teach the brawl:

Beneath it all...

Please take my business card.

MELVIN'S TALENT AGENCY
A Division of Melvin's Media MEGACORP, LLC
MELVIN the FROG
Universal C.E.O. Times Infinity

I'll be handling Naomi's negotiations from now on.

But **PLEASE!!!**

I must protect my client!

Any questions may be submitted to me—**IN WRITING!**

But {GOOD DAY, SIR!

Yeah, but {I SAID, GOOD DAY!

See, Daddy?

Melvin and Naomi are Best friends now!!!

And it's all because of **YOU!**

With Your talent and my business savvy...

CAN Melvin and Naomi Remain besties?

WILL FLIPPY Ever Stop worrying?

And **WHO** Are the special Guest Stars Dashing forth to investigate ???

FIND OUT IN OUR *NEXT* EPIC ADVENTURE!

CAT KID COMIC CLUB

BOOK 3 COMING SOON!

NOTES & FUN FACTS

⭐ Squids really **DO** spray ink when they feel threatened or scared. It's made of melanin, and it's usually blueish-black in color (not purple).

⭐ Frankie, Boo, Brutus, and C.C. were all named after breakfast cereals.

⭐ Naomi's dialogue on page 157 (panels 3 and 4) was based on a quote from Olivia Chaffin, a Girl Scout from Tennessee who boycotted the sale of Girl Scout cookies because they contain some palm oils that are linked to deforestation. Her online petition made international headlines.

⭐ Chubbs and Jake's van is outfitted with an **ACTUAL WORKING DISCO** inside, including functioning stereo speakers, a mini subwoofer, 1970s faux-wood paneling, multicolored rotating disco lights, and a mirrored floor.

⭐ The Baby Frog Squad's spaceship had to be rebuilt after the original one (from book #1) got sat on accidentally.

⭐ The newly redesigned spaceship was made out of cardboard, duct tape, wire, hot glue, and magnets (which hold the legs up when in "flying mode"). The eyes are plastic light bulb-shaped flashlights and they really light up!

⭐ The little cars in BABY FROG SQUAD were made from the tops of Japanese salt containers (taped together) with rice-dough lips and toy "building block" wheels duct-taped underneath.

⭐ On page 140, Summer really **is** writing the Zen Shodo phrase, "Za Ichi So Shichi,"[1] which translates to "Sit First, dash Seven." It means: Start the day with meditation/prayer/mindfulness before dashing around.

---

1. Shozo Sato, Shodo: The Quiet Art of Japanese Zen Calligraphy (Rutland: Tuttle Publishing, 2014).

GET READING W